Harvey Rabbit

Illustrated by Gill Guile

By Terry Dinning

Brimax Books · Newmarket · England

It is a lovely Spring day. Harvey Rabbit and his friends are spring cleaning their homes. Harvey Rabbit cleans his burrow.

Olly Owl cleans his nest.

Morris Mouse cleans his hole.

Freddie Frog cleans the leaves from his pond.

Baby Bear helps Mrs Bear to clean their cave.

Harvey Rabbit is in his garden. He puts his rug over the washing line. Harvey beats the rug with his broom. Olly Owl flies down from his tree.

"What are you doing, Harvey?" he asks.

"I am cleaning my rug," pants Harvey.

Dust flies everywhere.

Freddie Frog leaps off his
lily pad.
"What are you doing, Harvey?"
he asks.
"I am cleaning my rug," puffs
Harvey. There is dust
everywhere.
Morris Mouse looks out of
his hole.
"What are you doing, Harvey?"
he asks.
"I AM CLEANING MY RUG!"
says Harvey.

The dust gets into Harvey's eyes. It gets into Morris' nose. It gets into Freddie's mouth. Everyone sneezes while Harvey cleans his rug.

"What are you doing?" asks a very small voice.

Harvey and his friends turn around and see a little lamb. They have never seen a lamb before.

"Hello," says Harvey. "Where do you come from?"

"I do not know," says the little lamb. "I am lost."

"We must find your home and take you back," says Harvey. "We will show you our homes. You can tell us if your home is like ours."

Off they go to Harvey's burrow. "Do you live in a burrow like this?" asks Harvey.

The little lamb looks at Harvey's burrow. Then he shakes his head. "Your home is very nice," he says, "but it is not like mine."

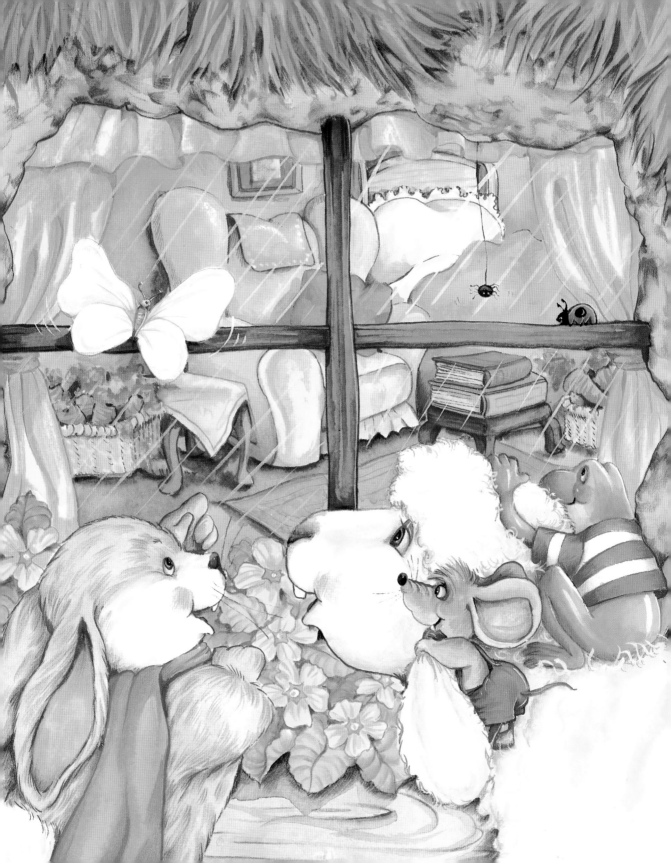

"Do you live in a nest?" asks Olly Owl.

"What is a nest?" asks the little lamb.

"Come and see," says Olly.

They go to Olly's tree.

Harvey points to Olly's nest up in the branches.

The lamb looks at Olly's nest. Then he shakes his head. "Your home is very nice," he says, "but it is not like mine."

"Do you live in a pond?" asks Freddie Frog.

"What is a pond?" asks the little lamb.

"Come and see," says Freddie. They go to Freddie's pond. Freddie jumps onto his lily pad. The lamb looks at Freddie's pond. Then he shakes his head. "Your home is very nice," he says, "but it is not like mine."

"Do you live in a hole?" asks Morris.

"What is a hole?" asks the little lamb.

"Come and see," says Morris. They go to Morris' hole.

The lamb looks at Morris' round hole. Then he shakes his head.

"Your home is very nice," he says, "but it is not like mine."

What can they do now?

"What about my home?" says Baby Bear. He lives in a cave with Mr and Mrs Bear. They all go to the cave.

"Do you live in a cave like this?" asks Baby Bear.

The lamb looks at the cave. Then he shakes his head. "Your home is very nice," he says, "but it is not like mine."

Baby Bear tells Mrs Bear all about their new friend.
"You silly things!" she says.
"This is a lamb! Lambs do not live in burrows or nests or ponds or holes or caves. Lambs live in big green fields."
Mrs Bear tells Olly to fly up into the air to see if he can find any big green fields with other lambs in it.

Up flies Olly, into the sky. He can see his friends below. Olly sees the tops of the trees. Then he sees a big green field with some lambs in it, just like their new friend. He flies back to the cave.

"Follow me," he says. "I have found your home, little lamb."

They all follow Olly. Soon they reach the big green field. The lamb sees his mother and runs to her. The lamb's mother is very pleased to see her baby. "Thank you for finding my lamb," she says.

"When I am big," says the lamb, "I will come and play with you again. Goodbye!"

Say these words again

cleaning	lamb
rug	lost
broom	branches
dust	lily
nose	sky
eyes	follow